Listen Up!

Diana Maxwell

HMS Tarlair and Memories of the Hawkcraig Admiralty Experimental Establishment Station, Aberdour, Fife, 1915-1918

First published in 2014 by Aberdour Cultural Association
New edition published in 2015 by Aberdour Cultural Association

ISBN 978-0-9929470-1-9

British Library Cataloguing in Publication Data
A catalogue record for this book is available from the British Library

This book is dedicated to Lewis Banks for his enthusiasm, support, advice, collection of additional information (especially photos), setting the layout and patiently seeing each stage through. Without Lewis's help I might never have completed the book.

Also dedicated to my grandchildren, Kyle, Daisy and Dylan, who are future custodians of Aberdour and her history.

About the author

Diana Maxwell was born in Edinburgh and has lived in Aberdour, Fife, where her grandparents lived, since she was five. She has two children, Euan and Shirley, and three grandchildren, Kyle, Daisy and Dylan, all of whom live in Aberdour.

She was a Superintendent Radiographer before retiring in 2013. Diana has always been a keen local historian and she has written articles, published locally, on "Aberdour in the First Half of the Century". Whilst researching this era she stumbled upon the fascinating find of the First World War Admiralty Experimental Establishment Station, HMS Tarlair, at Hawkcraig in her home village of Aberdour. What was more amazing was that the person in charge of the base (Captain Cyril P Ryan) had lived in her house, Hawkcraig Cottage. Diana appeared on the BBC "Coast" programme where one of the Tarlair experiments was re-enacted and also featured in the BBC's "War at Sea: Scotland's Story", 2015. Diana has also published an article, "Radiology in The Great War" (2014).

About the new edition

The primary difference between the original and new editions of "Listen Up!" is the inclusion of a supplement (pages 45-68 in the new edition) containing information that came to light following publication of the 1st edition in 2014.

Website

A website has been set up to accompany the new edition and this will be updated with any further information that becomes available: www.hmstarlairfife.org.uk.

Foreword

This volume by Diana Maxwell describes in detail the Hawkcraig Admiralty Experimental Establishment Station in Aberdour, Fife during the First World War. It is a valuable addition to our knowledge about this little known, but important research station.

The German Unterseeboot ("undersea boat") was an incredibly powerful weapon during the First World War. In the four months between October 1916 and January 1917 1.4 million tonnes of Allied shipping was sunk by these vessels. Most notoriously on 7th May 1915 the Germans breached international law and sank the ocean liner RMS Lusitania, a non-military ship, causing the deaths of 1,198 passengers and crew.

The work done at the Hawkcraig Point Station to develop a tool to assist in the defeat of the German U-boot menace was an incredibly important part of the Allied war effort.

The author, a retired Superintendent Radiographer, deserves high praise. Her dedication to this project is evident on every page. She has spent many hours researching local records and visited every inch of land over which the centre was located. The personal accounts of those who remember the Station and the photographs bring the whole story to life. This is altogether a well researched, moving and readable volume telling the story of a relatively minor Research Station, which had effects far beyond those that might at first have been imagined.

This book should be seen as a tribute to the Civil and Military Scientists together with their Researchers who contributed to some major technological advances in detection of the German U-boot.

Mr E R R Dunstan MBBS, BSc, FRCS (T&O)
Clinical Lead Orthopaedics, NHS Fife
Appraisal Tutor NES Scotland
Author of "The Forgotten Battle of Herouville"
Special Interest, The development of Trauma Surgery in WW1

Edinburgh 2014

Introduction

At the beginning of the First World War the German U-boat (*unterseeboot* or submarine) had become a major threat. Its large-scale destruction of merchant shipping caused not only great loss of life but also a fear that the British population would be fatally starved of materials and food. At one stage there were only six weeks of food reserves left (April 1916).

Between 1915 and 1918 the Admiralty Experimental Establishment Station located at Hawkcraig Point in the Firth of Forth's coastal village of Aberdour, Fife was the centre of a highly concentrated effort to defeat the German U-boats. It was the Navy's main hydrophone research and training base. The naval establishment was named HMS Tarlair. The Hawkcraig experiments were under the command of Captain Cyril P Ryan, RN who lived at Hawkcraig Cottage (where the author now resides). The hydrophones (underwater microphone receivers) comprised a microphone enclosed between two diaphragms which vibrated when there was a pressure change caused by a sound wave. By rotating the hydrophone, the operator was able to listen for propeller and machinery noises that might indicate the presence of a submarine. These were the forerunner of today's sophisticated sonar systems.

Cyril P Ryan serving at HMS Tarlair (left) and pictured c. 1910 (right)
Note the promotion from Commander (right) to Captain (left)

The staff from HMS Tarlair were also responsible for fitting submarines with hydrophones and issuing special sets of hydrophones to the 1,500 drifters and motor launches in the Auxiliary patrol, which was the major part of the Navy's anti-submarine force.

Little now remains of the experimental station HMS Tarlair at Hawkcraig Point, Aberdour. A few hut bases and relics of an old stone pier are all that can be seen. Originally there were up to sixteen huts of varying sizes, all constructed of wood. The research station had been set up at Granton, on the south of the Forth near Edinburgh, but moved in June 1915 to Hawkcraig Point on the north. The site was chosen because there was a deep-water channel protected by an anti-submarine boom.

RN Research Station HMS Tarlair as it was in 1917

The work carried out at HMS Tarlair is of local and national interest. During its short period of operation, major technological advances were achieved. It was one of the first instances of collaborative work between civil and military scientists and researchers. Investigation has uncovered a significant amount of archive and published material and the author has carried out her own original research to compile the information in this publication. She is grateful for all the help and assistance she has received from many different people.

This is not only the story of the development of technology, but also of the characters and personalities involved.

Views of Hawkcraig Point now and then

The following photographs show that, despite the extensive area covered by the base, hardly any trace remains.

Looking west-northwest 2014 (top) and 1917 (bottom)
All that remains of these huts are one or two concrete bases

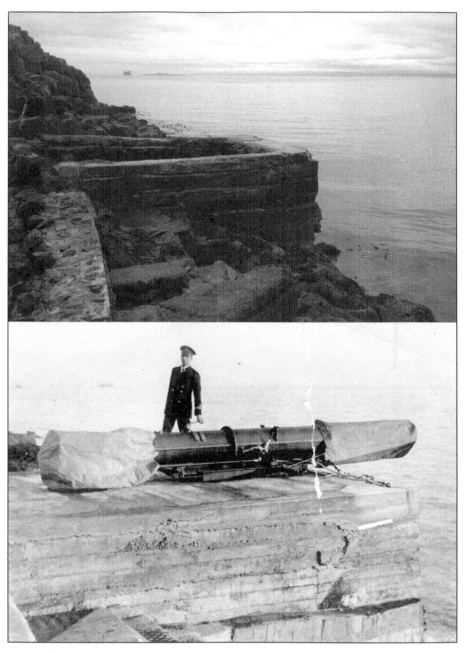

*Remains of the old concrete pier 2014 (top) and
the pier in use in 1917 (bottom)*

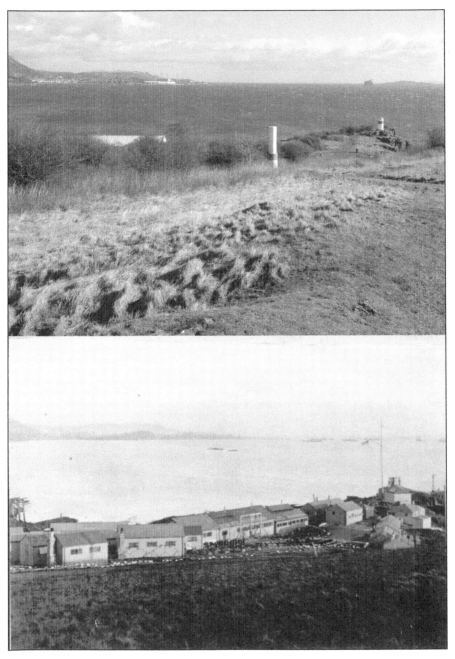

Looking towards Burntisland 2014 (top) and 1917 (bottom)

HMS Tarlair and the Hawkcraig experiments

HMS Tarlair was the Navy's main hydrophone research and training base throughout the First World War. 1,090 officers and 2,731 ratings attended courses there or were trained off site by travelling teams of instructors from Hawkcraig. By the end of the war 650 ratings and 120 officers manning 31 hydrophone stations at home and abroad, including ships, were attached to HMS Tarlair.

8" Dia. approx.

Prior to 1914, in the years following the building of the Royal Navy's first submarines (known as Holland submarines, after their designer J P Holland), very little effort had been made to locate enemy submarines. A Hervy-Gardner hydrophone had been produced by these two naval men but it was a very elementary device, which suffered from too much interference from water. The main problem facing those concerned with anti-submarine tactics was that very little was known about the acoustic properties of sound waves in water.

An improved hydrophone designed at HMS Tarlair

The name most closely associated with the Royal Navy's development of the hydrophone is that of Captain Cyril Ryan. He was an Irishman who joined the navy as a cadet in 1889. His career had been unremarkable until he took an interest in the then new invention of wireless telegraphy while serving in the Mediterranean in 1903. He subsequently made some useful contributions to the design of naval wireless installations. In 1911 he decided to retire from the navy and joined the Marconi Company. This allowed him to carry out more research in the field of wireless communications.

Following the outbreak of the First World War, Ryan was recalled to active service and sent to Inchkeith, an island in the Firth of Forth, where he began his experiments in the use of submerged hydrophones. Early in 1915 he had made such good progress that the Admiralty decided to support his work and the drifter HMD Tarlair was commissioned as a seagoing trials ship. Its name was later adopted as the "official" name for the research station.

HMD Tarlair

A small hut was set up at Granton as the first headquarters of what was to become a major organisation by the end of the war. In June 1915 a hut was erected on Hawkcraig Point, Aberdour, Fife and this was the foundation of the Hawkcraig Admiralty Experimental Establishment Station and training establishment.

Hawkcraig was chosen because it was adjacent to a deep-water channel protected at one end by an anti-submarine boom, a depth variation of between 30 to 126 feet and a tidal current of between ½ and 4 knots. The Forth was a busy shipping area and under favourable weather conditions the larger ships of the battle squadron based at Rosyth could be picked up on hydrophones 10 to 12 miles away. Admiral Beatty, who was in command of the Battle Squadron and later in charge of the Grand Fleet, was a strong supporter of Ryan and his work.

The experiments at Hawkcraig attracted some of the top civilian scientists of the day. Mr Albert Beaumont Wood DSc worked on the Hawkcraig experiments from 1915 to 1917. He had graduated with honours in Physics and had been researching into atomic physics at Manchester University under Professor Sir Ernest Rutherford (possibly the UK's leading scientist), along with other well-known physicists such as Mosely, Darwin, Geiger, Bohr, Marsden and Bateman (to name just a few).

Conducting hydrophone trials on HMD Tarlair

When the war broke out Wood was considered indispensable. The Admiralty Board of Invention and Research (BIR) and Rutherford suggested to Wood that naval research, in particular detection and location of submarines, would be more in his line than learning to fly! The two then carried out several experiments on underwater sound. Harold Gerrard, a lecturer in electrical engineering, also worked on the experiments. This preliminary work continued until Gerrard and Wood received their official appointments in October 1915 as physicists to BIR at the then remarkable salary of £1 per day, and they were posted to Hawkcraig, Aberdour to work on the Hawkcraig experiments.

They left Manchester on 17th November 1915 for Aberdour. A drifter met them at Granton and "took us across the Forth direct to Hawkcraig, a rocky promontory on the north side of the Forth and adjoining the little seaside village of Aberdour." There they met Captain Ryan, his secretary, Lt. Cdr. Ashley Froude, and other officers of his staff. A few days later Rutherford visited Hawkcraig. Wood was amazed that Ryan had never heard of the great

Rutherford prior to his arrival. Apparently, naval and civilian scientists did not normally associate with each other! Ryan demonstrated his hydrophones. They went out on the HM Drifter Hiedra, which was the vessel nominated for Wood and Gerrard's use, although still under Ryan's command. Soon after this visit Rutherford returned with Sir Richard Paget, a famous musician, and Mr. Gordon who was totally blind and had developed a sense of "absolute pitch". He could listen to moving ships using Ryan's moored hydrophones and some portable ones lowered over the gunwale of the Hiedra.

Albert Wood (pictured left) admitted that at the time of their arrival at Hawkcraig their knowledge of underwater sound was very primitive and that they were very impressed by Ryan's achievements in designing and making successful moored and portable hydrophones. Ryan had made valuable initial progress but knew little or nothing about the theory of sound or the possibilities of designing equipment which would indicate the direction of sound. He had, however, fitted submarines with pairs of hydrophones, one for port and another for starboard. They could indicate, to a trained ear, the approximate bearing of another ship, using the sound screening properties of the hull of the submarine. In selecting the hydrophone pairs, he enlisted the assistance of the most famous musicians in the country, Sir Hamilton Harty (conductor of the Hallé Orchestra) and his wife Agnes Nicholls, a famous soprano. They sat amongst a pile of hydrophones using a little hammer to tap the steel diaphragms and arranging them in pairs as "port low" and "starboard high"! The couple lived in a flat above Wood in Aberdour.

When listening to the sound of moving ships through Ryan's hydrophones the sound came mainly from the propellers, modulating the power drive of the ship. This enabled different ships to be identified: smaller ships, such as trawlers with reciprocating engines, had a characteristic beat due to the engines, while destroyers and larger ships fitted with turbines emitted a continuous rushing sound. All the ships' sounds appeared to have a predominant frequency, but as this frequency changed from one hydrophone to another it became obvious that this was due to the hydrophone diaphragm, rather than the sound from the ship. Ryan's work up to this point had been made without measurements of the sensitivities of the hydrophones and the ranges at which sound could be heard in the sea. He preferred to rely on his mental impressions, in spite of the fact that these were dependent on the conditions of the sea and other factors outwith his control.

RNVR Officers HMS Tarlair, C P Ryan 2nd Row, 3rd from left

Captain Ryan's staff at Hawkcraig consisted mainly of Royal Navy Volunteer Reserve (RNVR) officers, two ratings and a few seamen. His secretary, Lt. Cdr. Ashley Froude, was an elderly man, the son of J A Froude the historian, author of Froude's *History of England* and biographer of Thomas Carlyle. Amongst others whose names have been forgotten, there was Lt. Hamilton Harty, as already mentioned; a famous violinist, Lt. Brett, and Lt. Rose, a London theatre manager. They gave a concert in the village hall for the staff and villagers. This gave the villagers of Aberdour top class London entertainment on their doorstep for only 2/6 (12½p) for the best seats! (A lot of money at that time.)

The list of staff would not be complete without mentioning Ryan's two dogs (seen in the previous picture). They were a white cairn terrier and a red water spaniel. They were most popular with all the staff. The terrier was a wanderer and a survivor: Ryan claimed that this dog had once been shot and buried by a gamekeeper, but had dug himself out and returned home to Hawkcraig! The spaniel was stone deaf and Wood was amongst the crowd who saw this dog standing over a lighted fuse of a charge due to explode when blasting rock for a new jetty at Hawkcraig. They threw stones at it, waved and shouted to no avail. As luck would have it, the fuse failed and the dog lived to see another day! The spaniel was also in the habit of stealing Ryan's lunch from the table in his private hut, until one day the beef steak was connected to a high voltage circuit. The poor dog was seen flying out of the hut at such a speed that his feet did not seem to touch the ground and his tail stuck firmly between his legs. He never stole his master's lunch again!

Tiffies – some of HMS Tarlair's RN Artificers

Other staff included "tiffies". Tiffy is short for 'Artificer', a naval engineering specialist. The rank of "Engine Room Artificer" was established in 1868 as the navy moved from sail to steam. Artificers handled the manufacture of many types of military hardware as well as working in military laboratories. The rank is now covered by Engineering Technician (ET), Marine Engineer (ME) and Weapons Engineer (WE).

While in Aberdour, Wood was introduced to Sir Richard Paget's amazing musical talents. On one occasion, Rutherford, Paget and Wood had a meal together after a day's experimentation at sea. After dinner Paget entertained them by playing the piano and singing: he improvised in grand opera style the song and accompaniment of one of Edward Lear's nonsense rhymes. Sometime later Wood attended a lecture on speech synthesis, which Paget gave at the National Physical Laboratory. His work on human speech is now well known. By using plasticine models or by cupping his hands and blowing through an artificial larynx he could produce artificial speech, to the delight of his audiences.

There were several experimental ships attached to the station at Hawkcraig: HM Submarine B3, HMD Tarlair, HMD Hiedra, Eros, Venture, Ida Adams, destroyer Dee, the patrol boat P33, the trawler Opulent and NYKR. NYKR was a small steam yacht used by Ryan in his experiments on radio control, hence the name "No Yachting Knowledge Required". In view of the fact that no valve amplifiers or rectifiers were available at that time, Ryan was very successful in his early efforts in the development of remote controlled navigation of a ship involving steering and engine speed.

The first experiments Wood and Gerrard performed at Hawkcraig involved various forms of sound receivers for use in the sea – these were "Broca" tubes, microphones and magnetophones mounted on diaphragms – and in testing out equipment sent to them from Manchester by Rutherford. They found that the predominant frequencies were due to those of the hydrophones. Early in 1916 Paget came to their aid to find a reliable frequency analysis of a submarine's propeller and he suggested listening direct with both ears under the water. This idea did not appeal to Wood or Gerrard, but Paget went out with a sailor in a small boat whilst a submarine was circling round it. Paget, who was able to tap his head to produce G sharp, leaned over the side of the boat and, with the sailor holding on to his legs, put his head under the water. When he came up he tapped his head and ran up the scale to the required note, which the sailor wrote down. This procedure was then repeated several times. Wood was not convinced that this was a very reliable method but was relieved that Paget did not develop pneumonia!

In 1916 they were fortunate in receiving one of the first three electrode valves, designed by Round of Marconi, which when correctly adjusted was a very efficient amplifier. This was a great leap forward, Wood and Bragg recommended that they should be incorporated into future equipment. Ryan disagreed as he considered that the technology needed further testing. The newly invented valves were in very short supply. Wood is recorded saying how he tried to save the first valves for demonstrations to "*visiting VIPs*". He was devastated when five of the first batch of six were "*burnt out*" during overly enthusiastic experiments. He was relieved when Bragg managed to obtained a new batch from Marconi.

One of the workshops

Ship towed hydrophones (Porpoises) developed at HMS Tarlair

Some experiments involved sound insulation tanks full of air-filled rubber tubes fitted to the port and starboard side of the Hiedra. They cut out a certain amount of sound interference from the ship but the propeller noise was still a problem. They observed various frequencies of the propellers and engine sounds of submarines at different speeds. Experiments were also made to devise a portable directional hydrophone; this was based on a model made and sent to Hawkcraig by Rutherford. They managed to produce a device with good bidirectional properties. In May 1916 Professor Bragg, and later Professor McGregor-Morris from East London College, arrived at Hawkcraig to work on the bidirectional hydrophones and went on to produce a unidirectional hydrophone.

A bidirectional hydrophone set awaiting testing, 1917

In addition to the frequent visits of Rutherford and Paget at Hawkcraig during this period, Admiral David Beatty and Lady Beatty and their son David were regular visitors, always showing great interest in the hydrophones and any ongoing laboratory experiments. In February 1916 Prince Louis of Battenberg accompanied them. The Duke of Buccleuch, who was chairman of BIR, also paid frequent visits. In May 1916 Professor Bragg, who had previously visited Hawkcraig with Rutherford and Paget, came as Resident Director of Research, bringing additional scientific staff: Sutton from Australia, Professor Hopwood from Bartholomew's Hospital, and Professor Bragg's secretary. He also brought additional mechanics: Menkins from Australia and Elliot from Leeds. In August of that year the following scientists arrived: Rigby, Burnside and Young from Bristol. In October, Boulding joined the staff. Dr Rankine became a frequent visitor and introduced the "photophone" to the programme of experiments (page 30). The day after Professor Bragg arrived Professor Duc de Broglie paid his first of several visits to Hawkcraig.

The Drawing Office HMS Tarlair

The Workshop HMS Tarlair

Wood stated that they would often watch and listen to Admiral Beatty's Battle Squadron as they sailed out to the North Sea from their base at Rosyth (on the Forth, west of Aberdour). On 1st and 2nd June 1916 they were devastated as they heard that some of Admiral Beatty's and Admiral Jellicoe's (who had both been at Hawkcraig only two weeks earlier) fine ships had been sunk and a large number of men lost after the Battle of Jutland. They witnessed the stragglers returning to Rosyth. Shortly afterwards, on 17th June 1916, King George V visited Admiral Beatty at Aberdour House, where Beatty lived during the war. He visited the experimental base and viewed experiments from a specially made glass tower overlooking the bay. The previous day Mr Asquith, the Prime Minister, visited Rosyth. These events impressed on the staff at Hawkcraig more than ever before the very important contribution their research was to the war effort.

HMS Tarlair at Hawkcraig was, from 1915, the Navy's major landmark in the development of scientific research. Unfortunately, the integration of civilian and service personnel was not without its problems. Ryan did not take kindly to the civilians who were not under his control. Harvey was also under the impression that the civilians would use his research to reap financial gain in the commercial world.

After the arrival of Professor Bragg and the increased scientific staff at Hawkcraig in May 1916, research was concentrated on improvements of the hydrophone and methods of making it unidirectional. This they achieved by using a disc as a baffle at a critical distance from the bidirectional hydrophone. Experiments were carried out in August 1916 using this hydrophone, with which they located the submarine G4 at a range of four miles. These portable detectors were immediately put into use searching for enemy submarines, and were the forerunners of today's sophisticated sonar systems.

The photographs opposite show some views of the huts at HMS Tarlair. These were taken by Mr Stevens, one of the scientists working at the base.

The Seagull proposals
(Featured on the BBC "Coast" series 3 episode 5)

BIR invited and received suggestions from scientists, naval personnel and members of the public on methods to combat the U-boat threat. This produced many bizarre ideas, but some of them were considered worth investigating; among these were proposals to train gulls to indicate the presence of U-boats.

Between 1915 and 1917, BIR considered Thomas Mills' proposal of using gulls and other birds to identify the presence of U-boats. Thomas Mills emigrated to Australia in the early 1860s and returned to England in the mid-1880s, having made his fortune as a gold mine pioneer and owner in Queensland. BIR eventually commissioned trials in summer 1917, but then decided to abandon the possibility. BIR continued to be approached by Mills, who carried out his own trials at his own expense and who became increasingly exasperated at BIR's reluctance to further consider a scheme which had become an obsession with him.

The Admiralty and BIR had considered training gulls to detect periscopes in 1915. It was proposed that merchant ships should tow a dummy periscope *'from which at intervals food would be discharged like sausage-meat from a machine'* to teach the birds to associate periscopes near ships with food, leading them to swoop on the periscopes of real submarines, therefore training them to follow and locate enemy submarines. Dr Chalmers Mitchell (Secretary of the Zoological Society of London) and Sir Charles Parsons of the Central Committee of BIR were keen to try the scheme, but Rear Admiral Duff, Director of the Anti-Submarine Division, was concerned that it could cause false alarms since the gulls might not respond to fish discharges from a model periscope and gulls were not found too far out at sea. However, the sub committee decided that a trial feeding mechanism should be devised.

In May 1917, at a BIR meeting presided over by Lord Fisher, it was reported: *'In consequence of a suggestion made by the Board of Invention and Research to test the possibilities of attracting seagulls to the periscopes of submarines by ejecting food therefrom and thereby training them to follow and locate enemy submarines, the Admiralty have approved an experiment being made in submarine B3 and have asked BIR to provide a suitable food box for the purpose'*. Paget, the secretary, reported that a Mr Carnegie was constructing an apparatus for intermittently feeding birds from a dummy periscope, to be fitted on B3 for trials in the Firth of Forth. W H Hudson, the ornithologist and popular nature essayist, had been invited to assist in the experiments. The idea of using pigeons was raised, as a ship could carry and control these birds and they could fly great distances. Paget replied that this idea had been considered before but had not been thought feasible by the officer in charge of the pigeon loft at HMS Excellent. Paget reported that a falconer had suggested the use of hawks, but this was considered impracticable.

These experiments were duly carried out at the Hawkcraig Admiralty Experimental Station where Captain Cyril Ryan was in charge. He was not convinced by the gull experiments and was, as predicted, uncooperative and obstructive. The approved programme of experiments was placed under the supervision of Richard Kearton, who was hopeful of success, but it was short-lived. In August 1917 the secretary reported to the sub committee that difficulties had arisen involving use of the Submarine B3 in these experiments, and the matter had been referred again to the Admiralty. The Third Sea Lord soon decided that the experiments should be dropped altogether. At the end of August, it was noted that the difficulties referred to were not necessarily due to technical or experimental problems, but those regularly experienced by civilian scientists and BIR staff when dealing with Ryan! Tension grew between BIR and the Admiralty in 1917. The Grand Fleet Secret Packs (held by The National Archives at Kew) provide some indication of the inevitable failure of the intended seagull experiments at Hawkcraig. Vice Admiral Peirse, who served on the Committee of BIR, had contacted the Commodore (Submarines) in July to report Kearton's suggestion that *'before attempting experiments with a food ejecting periscope, it would be advisable to begin with hand feeding experiments from B3'*. A few days later, Kearton wrote to Ryan: *'I have been asked by Vice Admiral Peirse to assist you in carrying out some experiments on seagulls in connection with Submarines'*, adding that he would like to photograph the accomplishments. The next day, Ryan complained to the Commander-in-Chief of the Grand Fleet, Admiral Sir David Beatty, who was based at Rosyth, lived in Aberdour, and who was a personal friend:

I have the honour to transmit for your information copy of a Reference Sheet from the Board of Invention and Research, forwarded to me by Commodore (S), Admiralty, suggesting that Submarine 'B.3' be employed for training seagulls to locate submarines, with a further letter received from the expert who it is proposed should supervise this work.

It is submitted:-

(1) That Submarine 'B.3' is constantly employed here...[on work related to hydrophones]

That the training of seagulls would interfere seriously with this work, and that the advantages that might be gained are so extremely doubtful, that it would be inadvisable for 'B.3' to be detailed for this purpose.

Beatty replied to Ryan on 27th July 1917, suggesting that the trials should not interfere with the hydrophone work, reassuring him that B3 was still under his orders, and asking Ryan to inform him if cooperation with Kearton had been inconvenient. It would appear that Ryan had already decided that such cooperation would indeed be inconvenient, and no record has been found of any actual use of B3 before the decision in August to abort the project.

It is unlikely that Ryan would cooperate, even if he had been ordered to, in an extended experimental programme with Thomas Mills. Encouraged by his own observations of the behavior of gulls in the presence of submarines off the south coast of England, Mills had sent his first letter to BIR in February 1917. His method below was considered at its meeting in April:

"Have a small float containing a dummy periscope; the float to contain a quantity of rough food, say dog or cat's flesh or any other food which will float on the water. The machine to discharge small quantities every few minutes so the birds will see the food floating on the sea. The float could be towed behind a vessel at a fair distance and made so it will sink, as when the tow-line break [to keep this secret method from the enemy]. I consider if the experiment was tried first near some port or near where the enemy submarines were working, I believe the birds in about two weeks would be thoroughly trained to fly around the periscope or over the wake of a submarine. I would suggest a small mirror or bright piece of metal placed on top of a dummy for the first few days to attract the birds. The experiment will cost a very small sum as you have the means of carrying it out. I hope you will

try it, that is, if it is not already in use. I would be very glad to give all the assistance I could or do it myself if I had the mechanical means in a suitable place and assistance from the Government, not in money".

Mills was informed that similar proposals had previously been considered. There was never any reference to Mills by name in BIR minutes. He decided to construct his own machine, having moved to Scotland.

By August 1917, when BIR decided to end its trials with submarine B3, Mills was ready to put his machine to the test, and he successfully sought an interview at the Royal Naval base at Granton with Admiral Starten, who stated that seagulls would not be able to distinguish between friendly submarines and U-boats. Mills was taken aback by this and subsequently advocated the retention of British and allied submarines in port, so that the use of trained gulls would not result in such a mistake. The destruction of the U-boat by his method was his main objective.

Testing a model of Thomas Mills' patented Sea Gull Decoy on the Firth of Forth, 2006 (image © Lewis Banks)

Mills was not deterred and continued his trials until September 1918. He approached and was rebuffed again by BIR in February 1918 when attempting to re-establish the credibility of his invention using Petrol Controllers. Mills wrote with details of his method to Thomas Edison (the great American inventor and businessman), but received a short reply suggesting he should make a more formal approach to the Naval Consulting Board!

In September 1918, Mills left Exmouth to return home to Sandhurst, believing that the role of the seagull in combating submarine piracy would remain essential for the future security of the civilized world.

Conclusion on the Seagull proposals
The relationship between the Royal Navy and the role of BIR was declining in mid-1917. BIR's willingness to consider imaginative and desperate possibilities for anti-submarine measures, such as the seagulls, made it vulnerable. These proposals represented a healthy inventiveness encouraged by crisis, but such acceptance of new ideas in a conservative naval environment was inevitably risky. With the vindication of convoys and then the development of Sonar soon after the end of the war, these ideas, already declassified and in the public domain, were quickly forgotten as embarrassments.

Seaplane station at Hawkcraig

There was a small military seaplane station at Hawkcraig, in the garden to the east of the Forth View Hotel. It operated from 1913 and continued until at least 1919. It comprised only a single aircraft hangar and at least one timber hut. The seaplane was launched down a very steep slipway across the shingle beach. Remains of the runway are rapidly eroding but still detectable.

The seaplane station

It is not surprising to find that seaplanes were based at Hawkcraig: they were also used to combat U-boats. When a U-boat was detected she was hunted by destroyers, motor boats and seaplanes. The motor boat engines were stopped so that the hydrophones could detect the position of the U-boat.

At the start of the Battle of Jutland in May 1916, when he first received reports of enemy vessels, Admiral Beatty ordered the launch of a seaplane to investigate. Heavy clouds forced the plane to fly at a mere 900 feet above the waves. The seaplane encountered four light cruisers which opened fire but failed to hit it. The pilot of this plane was F J Rutland, who earned the nickname "Rutland of Jutland". Although this sighting had no marked effect on the battle, Beatty was to write that the sighting did, *"indicate that seaplanes under such circumstance are of distinct value"*.

One of the main duties of the Royal Navy Air Service (RNAS) was to aid in the battle against the U-boat. The RNAS employed both seaplanes and non-rigid airships to carry out reconnaissance missions. The airships were slower, but could carry the bulky wireless transmitters which were too heavy for the seaplanes.

The aim of these missions was to force the U-boats underwater as much as possible, in order to make them more vulnerable to attack when they were forced to the surface to recharge their batteries. As the war progressed the RNAS began to use the seaplanes offensively against the U-boats as well. In May 1917 the UC36 was the first submarine to be sunk by an aircraft. The UB20 suffered a similar fate in July and the UB32 in August.

The Royal Navy wanted to equip ships with aircraft which could intercept the German Zeppelins. Experiments proved that seaplanes, weighed down by their large floats, could not provide the required performance. The "Pup" plane was produced, which required a very small take off run (20 ft). The Navy revived the idea of flying wheeled aircraft from decks. F J Rutland, who had flown the reconnaissance mission at Jutland, flew the first such plane from the decks of the Manxman and Campania. The Navy subsequently fitted light cruisers with such take off platforms. The "Pups" had to be supplied with special airbags to keep them afloat if they had to land on the sea, when land was too far away, until the ship's crane could lift them back up on deck.

The launch of the seaplane at Hawkcraig

From a personal account in "Hush; or, The hydrophone service" by Herbert Wilson who, as an RNVR officer, served at HMS Tarlair:

The Captain's orders are to get out the seaplane. "I want all the men I can get." Follow me but a few steps to the hangar behind the listening hut.

Inside of the hangar a crowd had gathered round the seaplane. The Chief is absolutely in his element, he lives for these occasions.

Chief: "Let her go a bit!" The winch begins to slack off cable. "Easy! Easy!! EASY!!!"

After five minutes' delay the coiled bight commences sulkily to retreat and brings two of the audience heavily to earth in the process. Meanwhile the seaplane has been pushed a few yards further seawards, and is by this time approaching the inclined plane of cement down which it must travel to the water. At last, after a severe struggle, the bight has been taken out, and the cable is again taut.

"Pay out! Pay out!! PAY OUT!! !"

Relentlessly, the winch continues to haul in, and slowly the seaplane retreats.

"Here, tell those darned idiots on the winch to pay out!"

**The Chief supervises the launch
of the seaplane**

After a brief delay the tension on the cable is eased again, and the beginning of the inclined plane is reached. Here a prolonged halt is called, and petty officers are placed by the Chief perched on the floats, while others are suspended, from every conceivable portion of the seaplane that would yield the necessary purchase, and from some that would not. 'Chief' has each and all of them weighed up to an ounce.

"Here you, you're too heavy on the float; come off, my lad, and change places with him."

So it was with the Chief. A petty officer he added here, another he shredded there, and deftly he filled the gaps of such as fell off through mis-adventure, until slowly the seaplane tilted on the slope. It was masterly and amusing. The casualties to date could hardly have exceeded what could have been counted on the fingers of both hands. Without further mishap, the monster on the trolley reaches the sea, and the carriage is cast off. The tiny wavelets lap gently against the floats, for the wind has completely died away, and with it the sea.

Divers appeared water-proofed from top to toe, and floats round their waists. Into the water they bravely dash to keep the seaplane straight, for she has now cast off from the cable and is on her own.

Halford starts the engine, and takes with him two of these poor fellows, who, for some reason, omit to let go. It is an agonizing moment, tense with drama! Chancing everything, they gallantly let go, and struggle ashore as easily as that burden of cork will permit.

Once afloat, it was soon evident that the seaplane would not, on this occasion, develop enough power to leave the water, although she would taxi, so back she had to come. Reverse the sequence for return journey, adding the extra time for several attempts to get her back on to the slipway. The brilliant idea did at last occur to someone to harness the tail of the plane to a dinghy, so as to keep her from swinging off.

When the seaplane successfully took off, below the circling plane was a motor launch. All of a sudden the motor launch might dash off as on some settled purpose. They looked on at what they called "A marvel of man's achievement!"

These were shared with distinguished visitors from all parts of the dominions and other countries, from the King downwards, "who visited our base, and saw the strange and wondrous things".

Nightly routine at Hawkcraig

Also from a personal account in "Hush; or, The hydrophone service" by Herbert Wilson:

Just look at the time, its five o'clock! I did tell you about that little affair of the seaplane? It is the hour when I should be able to down tools, for tonight my section's on night duty in the listening hut. Some of us condemned this night duty routine unreservedly.

Here you have a hydrophone station whose functions are purely instructional and experimental, tucked away in a remote corner of the Forth, as immune from attack as it is capable of. Why keep men out of their beds to maintain a continuous hydrophone watch, religiously logging every engine sound they may imagine they hear through the long night?

It seems to me that these people missed the point. In the first place this occasional discomfort was nothing very much to grumble at. Most of both officers and men were destined for shore hydrophone stations, and were merely rehearsing here what they would have to undergo there. In normal times your turn would not repeat itself oftener than weekly at the worst. However, it's my turn to-night, so I had better get right along now. With the exception of an hour's interval for the evening meal, I must be in the neighbourhood of this hut until 9 a.m. the next morning.

During the course of the evening a friend comes down to help cheat the weary hours. Incidentally I tell my friend that there is a rumour that the Captain will land at the wooden pier at eleven tonight, as he is coming across from Leith in the motor launch.

"Look here!" says my friend, "I bet you you won't tick off the Captain. "What do you mean? "

"Just this. What's to prevent you marching down the pier – you're on duty you know – when you hear the motor launch, you're not supposed to know that it is the Captain, to deal with some unknown trespasser on Admiralty property."

I tell my friend that the idea is good, and will receive my official consideration. The hours pass, my friend has gone, I have consumed much cake, sandwich, cocoa, etc., and reached that stage of repletion that will ensure my getting no sleep, not that I expect any.

"There's the motor launch, Sir," says my section leader, and at the same time I hear the familiar "chug chug" of the petrol engine, every moment becoming louder.

26

Determined that duty is duty and must be done, I grope my way down the wooden pier, reaching the end almost simultaneously with the motor launch. The moment has arrived! Now or never! What then do I do? I hope that I have as much pluck as most people, but I am a coward and so I do nothing and say nothing! I help to tie up the motor launch, and the Captain walks past me, with a genial "good night," on his way to Hawkcraig Cottage!

It is midnight, so I had better get one of my three visits to the sentry out of the way. Up the Heath Robinson's steps, to the higher level I must go, and it is so dark. I have no torch. Surely my courage is vindicated! Here is the true, the higher type of courage. That little incident of the Captain! What of it! What was that? I start, stumble, and nearly fall over the brink, my skin a tingling with terror. A moment's pause to sort myself, and I am again the man! What happened? It was dark at the time, and it was difficult to judge. Possibly a rat. On the other hand, may be still some smaller member of the rodent tribe. The incident must now be considered to be closed.

I find that the sentry's insomnia is not near as aggravated as my own, fortunate fellow!

Into the listening hut again. To avoid treading on the slumbering bodies of the section, scattered on the dusty floor, requires the agility of a sword dancer.

One thing makes this watch nearly worthwhile. The early morning visit to the sentry if it is fine.

I cannot give you the beauty of the dawn from Hawkcraig. The range of tint from rose in the low east to the dark purple of the hills over against Burntisland, minute by minute diluted in depth, as the shafts of light that herald the rising sun lend transparency. The sea is smooth as a pond, and the pearl grey mists soften the outlines of the colliers lying out in the bay. The entirety is a picture that will hold you until a warning shiver bids you stay no more.

A further period of wakefulness brings the hour of seven, when you long to retire to The Forth View for a bath. In time of peace an hotel. During the war it sheltered a goodly part of the ship's company.

When at last nine comes, and with it morning Divisions, you are free to go your way in peace.

The shore hydrophone stations

Shore hydrophone stations were under the command of HMS Tarlair at Hawkcraig where all ranks of officers received their training in order to take their allotted place at one of the stations already in commission, or soon to become so.

The main component of a shore hydrophone station was the listening hut, and these stations were located round the coast of the British Isles, Ireland and in the Mediterranean.

From the listening hut ran from eight to sixteen insulated cables, to distances varying from two to ten miles, where the ends joined up with the tripods supporting the hydrophones resting on the sea bed.

Hydrophone on tripod support, HMS Tarlair, 1918

When the stations were laid, it seemed to be convenient that the cables should be brought to the margin of the water in a bundle, and fanned out as individual cables from there. This course seemed particularly to be indicated if the station was perched on the top of a cliff, cut by a convenient cleft or gully, which would offer some protection to the cables, as well as affording access to the shore for the station operators. Attached to the base were eight or so armed drifters, drawn from the Scottish and East Coast fishing centres, especially fitted for the purpose of cable laying and repairing. The only limitation of the shore station was in the maximum cable length of ten miles.

Hydrophone training:
In the converted hold of a drifter (top)
At Hawkcraig, 1918 (bottom)

The Photophone

Professor Alexander O Rankine from University College London introduced the photophone (a method of communicating across long distance by the modulation of a beam of light by speech) to the programme of scientific investigations. This involved fitting up a transmitting mirror at Hawkcraig and a receiving mirror on Inchcolm Island, one and a half miles away.

To simplify the theory of the photophone: It operated a speech-modulated beam of light, transmitted by a large convex lens (mirror). The lens on a small concave mirror attached to a gramophone sound box or telephone earpiece focused the light from a point light source. The light diverged and passed through a similar lens, which projected the beam to a distant receiver. There, two similar grids were mounted, one in front of each lens. An image of the first grid was superimposed on the second by reflection in the small concave mirror. This caused the latter to oscillate under the vibrations of speech, as the dark spaces of the image grid moved over the openings of the second grid producing fluctuations of intensity of the light beam. This was collected at the receiving end by a mirror or lens and focused on a photoelectric selenium cell in a circuit with a battery and a telephone earpiece. The resistance changes of the selenium resulted in the reproduction of the original sound in the receiving telephone (without an amplifier!). When the light beam from Hawkcraig was picked up at Inchcolm the speech was easily audible and of good quality. It was, however, very frustrating to the operators at both ends when the beam was not accurately directed and there was no alternative means of communication between the two points.

Professor Bragg managed to persuade Captain Ryan to lay a spare length of hydrophone cable to be used as a telephone line between the two photophone stations. This enabled the two points to be in continuous audible contact, which was a marked improvement. Unfortunately, only two weeks later when Professor Bragg was attending a meeting in London, Captain Ryan ordered one of his officers to take the cable away. He did not even apologise to Professor Bragg!

There was a continuing rivalry between the two camps. On one occasion when Bragg was out on HMD Hiedra, he asked the skipper to perform a certain manoeuvre. When the ship returned to Hawkcraig, Ryan disciplined the skipper even although Bragg apologised for having asked the skipper to make the manoeuvre.

There were allegedly several amusing incidents which occurred during the photophone experiments: Wood recalled that one day when he was out in a boat 50 or 100 yards from the transmitting end of the photophone on Hawkcraig, he heard the operator saying *"I am speaking softly now"*, and he wondered what was the advantage of using the photophone!

The photophone was designed for use as a short-range communication device between ships of a fleet, but was apparently never used for this purpose. The photophone method of modulating a beam of light by speech was, however, used after the war by Rankine for recording speech on film, which was used in the development of the first "talking" films which were then in their infancy.

The final experiments before the split

Ryan and the scientists carried out experiments with towed hydrophones with little success. Nash, of Western Electric Company, Woolwich, visited Hawkcraig in 1916 for advice and discussions. He eventually produced a "fish" containing the unidirectional hydrophone (which was developed at Hawkcraig), remotely controlled from the ship, for which he claimed an award at the end of the war.

Ryan also made preliminary tests of a depth-sounding bomb. The depth was to be determined from the time of the fall of the bomb from the water surface to the bottom. The impact on the bottom was indicated by an explosion of a small charge. However, methods of detecting the time taken to reach the bottom were unsuccessful; they included detecting echoes with an oscillator and calibration methods.

William Duddell visited Hawkcraig at this time and tested the sound analysis experiments using his vibration galvanometer. Although he died soon afterwards, he wrote a report on detecting submarines by electrical and electromagnetic means.

Other visitors to Hawkcraig in late 1916 were:

Vice-Admiral Sir Richard Peirse, Admiral Commander in Chief at Rosyth.

Sir Joseph Petaval, Professor of Engineering, Manchester, and, from 1919, Director of the National Physical Laboratory, Teddington.

Richard Threlfall, who later invented the "sticky" (phosphorus or incendiary) bullets which spelled the fate of the hydrogen filled Zeppelins.

Captain Bragg, Professor Bragg's son, visited Aberdour in 1916 on one of his home leaves from France. It was shortly before this that the Braggs received the Nobel Prize (Physics) for their work on X-rays and crystal structure.

Towards the end of 1916 it was clear that the civilian and service scientists would make more progress if they were to separate. When Bragg explained the situation to Lord Balfour, the latter suggested that Ryan should be moved! Bragg replied that perhaps the civilian staff should move as Ryan was there first.

On 26th December 1916 Bragg and his family, with all the staff, left Hawkcraig to start a new Admiralty Experimental Station at Parkeston Quay, Harwich.

Wood and Young stayed behind to complete their experiments on the acoustic properties of sound in water, at Cullaloe reservoir, near Aberdour. They finally left Aberdour and re-joined their staff at Parkeston Quay in March 1917, after successfully completing the sound-field experiments with the direction finder and baffle. In connection with depth sounding bombs, they visited the navigating officer on HMS Lion at Rosyth; Captain Strutt, son of Lord Rayleigh. He described to them an incident during the Jutland battle, while he was fortunately on the bridge, when a shell passed through his cabin and exploded further inside the ship. The heat from the shell destroyed everything inside his cabin except his iron bedstead and the ends of his golf clubs!

The civilian scientists concluded that it had been a very fruitful (though relatively short) stay at Hawkcraig, Aberdour between November 1915 and March 1917. They had learnt much about the sea and the propagation of sound in it. They soon proved the fact that the velocity of sound in the sea was approximately four and half times that in air and that wavelengths were increased in the same proportion. They learnt more about hydrophones, microphones and magnetophones. They were surprised to find how far sound could travel through water, when they detected the noise of a large ship's propeller at 10 or 12 miles. They discovered ways of obtaining sound direction underwater using devices considerably smaller in linear dimensions than the wavelength of the incident sound.

In retrospect, they felt that they derived a real benefit from their association with such a diverse mixture of men all working towards the same purpose. These included RN and RNVR officers, engineers and university scientists who all had a lot more in common than they would admit and learnt much from each other.

HMS Tarlair at Hawkcraig after the split

Hawkcraig remained the Navy's main hydrophone and research training base throughout the war. 1,090 officers and 2,731 ratings attended courses there or were trained by instructors from Hawkcraig. By the end of the war the Tarlair establishment (Hawkcraig) numbered 650 ratings and 120 officers, manning 31 hydrophone stations at home and abroad. Ships were also attached to Hawkcraig.

HMS Motor Torpedo Boat 326 which was seconded to HMS Tarlair

HMS Tarlair staff fitted ship-borne hydrophones to submarines, and special sets were issued to the 1,500 drifters and motor launches in the Auxiliary patrol. These vessels formed the backbone of the Navy's anti-submarine force. The development and manufacture of the hydrophones, and the training of their operators, was led by the staff of HMS Tarlair.

The training had been successful. The first known U-boat, the mine layer UC-66, was sunk as a direct result of being detected by hydrophones in April 1916 by the Lizard Hydrophone division. A witness said the sea boiled! We have an account about another successful pick up, as on 25th October 1918 the telephonist Geoffrey Clough, on watch in HM submarine G2, picked up underwater transmissions made by the German submarine U78. By the strength of the acoustic signal he enabled the G2 to be guided towards the German U-boat, which was torpedoed as she lay on the surface.

Ryan continued to develop the hydrophone and especially a fish type of towed hydrophone (the Eel), which was accepted by the Admiralty in October 1917. The Porpoise was Ryan's most advanced hydrophone, which came into production in September 1918.

Ryan devised fixed seabed surveillance installations. This involved a microphone to be mounted on a tripod base then connected to the shore by an insulated cable terminating in a listening hut. He also produced hydrophone buoys which could be moored 40 feet below the surface, but ideally 18 feet, where tides and currents were not a problem. However, patrol vessels and other craft using the area had to be strictly monitored so as not to cause a false alarm.

Hydrophone mines were another anti-submarine device designed by Ryan. A magnetophone was placed in a mine in series with detonators and a firing circuit. The magnetophone was activated by sound waves, which caused variations in the magnetic field. This produced a small current to be sent out along the cable to the receivers at the controlling station. The range of audibility was 200 yards.

Magnetophone mine

The first shore controlled minefields making use of the magnetophone and hydrophones were laid in mid-1916. They were known to have accounted for the destruction of two U-boats and possibly two others. The last U-boat to be sunk in the First World War was UB116. She was destroyed on 28th October 1918 when passing over the magnetophone minefield at Scapa Flow.

By the end of 1918 it was possible to look back on very significant progress in the field of underwater detection. However, the problem of defining the exact depth and position of the submarine remained, which was solved with the coming development of the Asdic or Sonar, as it is now known.

The final tally of World War I proved that six U-boats sank as a direct result of hydrophone contacts (UC3, UC49, UC66, U78, UB107 and UB115). The large number of anti-submarine vessels fitted with detection devices also made a very significant contribution to the harassment of the U-boats and the development of anti-submarine tactics. In 1918 there were 54 sightings of U-boats in which hydrophones played a part.

Ship towed "fish" hydrophones (Porpoises), 1918

Clearing minefields in the Firth of Forth, 1919
(the lighthouse in the picture is the Oxcars lighthouse)

The closing down of the Hawkcraig Experimental Base

Edward J Trillo, Chief Gunner, RN, was stationed at HMS Tarlair and he was in charge of the closure of the station in 1919. He resided with his wife and family at 7 Manse Street, Aberdour. The author met Edward Trillo's son, Robert (Bob), when he was on holiday with his wife, Moira. They had come to Aberdour to visit the place where his father had been stationed during and just after WW1.

Bob Trillo found a letter which his father Edward Trillo had written to his wife, 19th January 1919:

"....more expensive to live at Aberdour than Elie, Aberdour is beastly dirty and the roads are so ill kept and it rains nearly every night. I am kind of deputy for Cmdr. Froude who I believe is leaving soon, he is R.N.V.R. I saw Ryan, he said he'd get the stripes and was trying hard to keep me but could not yet guarantee, from what I know of him I think I can depend on it."

One of the problems with the Navy in those days was that people were moved about as if they were counters on a Snakes and Ladders board. The above

extract was when Edward's wife was still living at 29 Park Place, Elie and he was staying at Seabank House, Aberdour. On 18th January 1919 Edward is recorded as "care of" Mrs. Milburn, 7 Manse Street.

E Trillo, Chief Gunner, RN, outside 7 Manse Street, Aberdour in 1919. In the pram is his son Eustace, born at 7 Manse Street on 4th Sept 1919.

Bob also provided some photos taken during his parents' stay in Aberdour and this most interesting document regarding the closing of the station:

FROM: The Commanding Officer, H.M.S. "Tarlair", Aberdour, Fife.

TO : The Commander in Chief, Coast of Scotland, R O S Y T H.

DATE: July 11, 1919.   REFERENCE: 362/19

SUBMITTED/

APPOINTMENT OF Mr. E.J. TRILLO,
Chief Gunner, R.N.

Mr E.J. Trillo, Chief Gunner, R.N., has been appointed to H.M.S. "Fearless" vice Mr. Barnes, Gunner, R.N., date of appointment, 4th July 1919.

Owing to the duties Mr Trillo has been employed upon, and in view of the Admiralty order dated 4th July to close down Harkcraig Experimental Station as soon as possible, it is requested that Mr. Trillo may be retained at Harkcraig for a period of one fortnight from the present date, before taking up his appointment, in order to clear up correspondence and assist at closing the Station.

Mr. Trillo, in February 1919, took over the duties previously carried out by Commander Proude, R.N.V.R., viz., Correspondence relating to all Contract work, and in charge of records of Experiments. In March he took over from Commander Hervey, R.N., the executive duties of the Station, supervision of Tenders and charge of Confidential Books, and the Demobilisation of Ratings.

The Office Staff has been reduced to one Civilian Clerk. The Officers now remaining at the Station are R.N.V.R., due for demobilisation, except Mr. G. Lee, Gunner(T), who is in charge of Stores.

CAPTAIN, R.N.

Edward J Trillo, RN, and his son Eustace at White Sands Bay (Silversands), Aberdour, May 1920

Two villagers' memories of WW1 (as told to the author as part of her oral history project, "Tales of Aberdour")

The King George V and Lloyd George's visit

Miss Rena McLauchlan 1896-1988 (former county councillor for Aberdour)

Rena recalled the First World War in Aberdour and all the naval activity in the Forth. She described "The Boom Defence", which was a net across the Forth from Inchcolm to Barnhill to prevent German submarines reaching Rosyth. It could be lifted up to allow our own ships and submarines to pass through. Admiral Beatty, Commander of the Naval Fleet at Rosyth, resided in Aberdour House and was host to many distinguished guests, including King George V and Lloyd George: they arrived at Aberdour harbour in the Admiral's steam barge, "The Lion". After disembarking they *walked* across the field from the harbour (the gateway can still be seen a few yards to the west of the foot bridge) to Aberdour House! Lady Beatty (formerly Miss Marshall-Field), the Admiral's wife, was an American millionairess. Rena McLauchlan remarked that she always wore a cloak and would walk down to the shore using a stick. She gave the village money for various good causes and funded the building of the original Institute to adapt it to accommodate sailors and soldiers and provide them with sleeping and washing facilities. The soldiers stationed on Inchcolm slept in hammocks in the Institute's billiard room when they had a night off.

Ryan may have invented the first remote control toy!

William Cuthill was born in Aberdour in 1913 and died aged 94 in 2008.

One of William Cuthill's earliest memories was of visiting Hawkcraig Cottage with his mother. The cottage was the home of Captain Ryan, who was in charge of the Hawkcraig Point Naval Experimental Base. Captain Ryan was a great inventor; he invented a toy dog which, after pressing a button, ran out of a box at one end of the lounge, encircled the room, and ran back into the box! William Cuthill loved to watch this toy, which in 1918 must have been years ahead of its time and possibly one of the first, if not the first remote control toy. William's mother was friendly with the Captain's house-keeper, Mrs. Anderson. She was popular with the village women folk because she told fortunes by reading tea leaves. William's mother was a frequent visitor to the cottage and, due to the attraction of the Captain's toy, William was always keen to accompany her. When William Cuthill came to see the author, it was his first visit to Hawkcraig Cottage since those days and as he looked round the cottage he found the rooms he visited as a child.

Another early memory was from 1918 at the end of the War, when William Cuthill was five years old. Admiral Beatty organised sailing trips around the Forth for the people of Aberdour on a small naval boat with one funnel. On one occasion they were taken to St Andrews, given tea at a Hotel and returned to the wooden pier in the evening, all with the Admiral's compliments.

During the First World War several concerts were held in the village to keep the troops happy. On one occasion the star was so popular, being the world famous pianist "Paderewski", that the Institute was too small to accommodate the audience, so the concert was staged in a field at the west end of the village. This was obviously another first for Aberdour, years ahead of "T in the Park"! Paderewski was touring Scotland at the time and agreed to play in Aberdour, much to the delight of the villagers. After organising this big event, there was a sudden panic in the village as there was no suitable piano for Paderewski to play! William Cuthill's mother came to the rescue and offered her brand new Daneman piano. Paderewski accepted her offer and had the piano transported into the concert field. The people of Aberdour were very proud the day Paderewski came to play in their village. They all had a very enjoyable and memorable evening. In 1919, in the newly independent Poland, Paderewski was appointed by President Pilsudski as the Prime Minister and Minister of Foreign Affairs (Jan 1919 – Dec 1919). He and Dmowski represented Poland at the Paris Peace Conference and signed the Treaty of Versailles.

Aberdourians and HMS Tarlair

Some local Aberdour people also worked at the base, including the brothers George and William Lyon and Dougie McLauchlan (Rena's brother).

Ship's Carpenters stationed at HMS Tarlair
PO William Lyon (second left), PO George Lyon (first right),
PO Dougie McLauchlan (second right)

William and George were part of the Aberdour family firm of "Lyon Brothers, Joiners and Undertakers" who had a workshop in Park Lane, Aberdour. It is known that George was in the Royal Naval Reserve, and it is likely that William was as well, and during the war the brothers were stationed at HMS Tarlair where they served as Ship's Carpenters.

After Sir William Bragg established his own department at HMS Tarlair, George Lyon was seconded to him to make his apparatus. Bragg was so impressed by George's work that when the civilian scientists left the base and Bragg moved, he asked George if he would move with him. George declined the offer, possibly because he didn't want to leave the family business or possibly because his wife was not too keen on moving south. A hundred years on, some of the brothers' descendants still live in Aberdour and the author is grateful to Annie Worrall, George's granddaughter, for identifying George, William and Dougie in the picture above.

Throughout their time at HMS Tarlair, the staff played an active role in the life of their host village, Aberdour, and were warmly welcomed.

Tarlair staff and Aberdour villagers take a little time for R&R

What happened to Captain Cyril P Ryan after WW1?

In 1917 Captain Cyril Percy Ryan was made a Companion of the Bath (CB), presumably in recognition of his services during the war (London Gazette 4/6/17). Ryan retired from the navy as a Captain in 1919. From the title deeds of the author's house, Hawkcraig Cottage, it appears that he kept his interest in Aberdour. In March 1920 he bought Hawkcraig Cottage for £680 and sold it in July 1922 when he moved to Southsea near Portsmouth.

Hawkcraig Cottage (on the left) and Hawkcraig House, 1918

The cottage on a winter's day on the Firth of Forth, 1918

In his memoir "The Crisis of the Naval War" Admiral of the Fleet Viscount Jellicoe wrote that, *"They were also greatly indebted to Capt. Ryan R.N., for the exceedingly valuable work carried out by him at the experimental establishment at Hawkcraig. Many brilliant ideas were due to Captain Ryan's clever brain."*

A patent search has revealed that following the war Ryan continued to apply his brain to a whole range of technical problems, many of them associated with his work in Aberdour, with at least twenty-four patents attributed to Ryan in the years leading up to 1934.

Some of the earlier patent applications (1916 to 1918) cover work that Ryan carried out at HMS Tarlair and include a patent for "Means of Controlling the Movement of Ships or other Mechanisms by wireless telegraphy" i.e. a radio controlled remote vehicle (see NYKR, page 12), and also sole and joint patents (one with W H Bragg and one with R G Harvey) for improved hydrophones. These wartime applications were granted but held from publication, presumably for reasons of secrecy, until 1928.

Contrast the image opposite, from Ryan's 1918 patent application "Improvements in Obtaining Direction of Subaqueous Sounds", with the pictures on pages 13/35.

Patents filed post-war in 1923 and 1924 show that Ryan continued to work on the development of systems for the detection of underwater sound and he is cited as a co-inventor with the Vickers Company on patents in this area as well as further developments in radio controlled mechanisms. On these patents Ryan is described variously as "Captain in His Majesty's Royal Navy ... of Woodlands, Droxfield, Hants" or "of Shotley House, East Molesey, Surrey".

Perhaps building on his experience with the "photophone" (see page 30), other patents show that after the war Ryan worked with the Fidelity Film Company of Wardour Street, London. There are patents granted in both 1933 and 1934 which cover the development of improved methods of recording sound onto film. Some of the techniques described are similar to those that could have been employed for an "improved" photophone.

In both 1922 and 1923 Ryan applied for a number of patents for improved designs of gramophone trumpets and sound boxes. The inventions described in these patents derive from Ryan's expert knowledge of the transmission of sound through solid objects and their surrounding media (in this case, air not water!). In these applications Ryan's address is given as Felton House, High Street, Portsmouth.

In 1921 Ryan applied for a patent covering "Electrical Means for Operating or Controlling Mechanisms by Sound". The nature of the invention is described as, *"relates to electrical means for operating or controlling mechanisms by sound. Whilst applicable to machines, it may also be employed for use in connection with toys such, for instance, as moving or running animals."* This description brings to mind the recollections of William Cuthill, as related on page 39, of having been entertained in Ryan's home by a mechanical toy dog which appeared to respond to Ryan's commands.

Some figures from the "toy" patent.
Is this the toy dog witnessed by William Cuthill?

Although the author has not researched Ryan's full history following the war, it is clear that he continued to be very active and inventive, often in collaboration with others who recognised the value of his *"clever brain"*.

Ryan died in his 65th year on 20th May 1940 in Topsham, Devon. He was survived by his wife Grace (nee Drury-Lowe), to whom he had been married since 1908, and his son (Percy) and daughter (Thelma Lucy).

SUPPLEMENT FOR THE NEW EDITION OF "LISTEN UP!"

Following the publication of the first edition of "Listen Up!" more information relating to the work at HMS Tarlair has been brought to the attention of the author and publisher, which has resulted in this supplement. We are grateful to all those who have supplied and helped compile this new material.

The supplement includes information on the following:

1. BIR 10071/16 Report by the Duke of Buccleuch, Lord Rutherford FRS and Sir R. Paget on visits to the Experimental Station under Commander Ryan RN, Granton on September 15, 16 and 21 1915 This report is held by The National Archives (ADM 293/4).

2. BIR 10064/16 Report on methods of collecting sound from water and determination of the direction of sound by Lord Rutherford FRS, Sept 1915 In this report Rutherford discusses hydrophones, magnetophones and submarine detection. It is held at the National Archives (ADM 293/7).

3. The Ettles Journal We are grateful to Jose Luis Eglinton for drawing our attention to the handwritten journal of Petty Officer L.J. Ettles who trained at HMS Tarlair and subsequently served overseas in the Hydrophone Service. Dave Wilkinson, the owner of the journal, has kindly gifted it to the author. We have reproduced the first six pages of the journal, in which Ettles writes of his time at HMS Tarlair. The transcript of these pages provides a vivid account of the experiences of the trainees at the base.

4. "Hamilton Harty Musical Polymath" by Jeremy Dibble This recently published work includes a transcript of an interview with Harty in 1934 in which he evocatively describes his "Listening Hut Experience". Thanks to Jeremy for alerting us to the interview, extracts from which are included in this supplement.

5. The Admiral Beatty Letters Admiral David Beatty was a prolific letter writer and this supplement includes details from two letters that specifically concern the work at HMS Tarlair and Beatty's very positive view of Ryan.

6. Alexander Crichton Mitchell Indicator Loop Trials at Hawkcraig Hydrophones were not the only anti-submarine technology trialled at HMS Tarlair. We are grateful to Mike Porter for telling us about the "indicator loop" submarine detection methods developed by Edinburgh scientist Alexander

Crichton Mitchell and of his experiments in the Forth. Mike introduced us to Dr Richard Walding, who has made a study of this technological development and is writing Mitchell's biography. Richard has kindly written a short article which is included in this supplement.

7. Honour and Service Rolls The service records of some of the men who served at HMS Tarlair and in the Hydrophone Service can be found in various "Rolls of Honour". The records for three of these men are included in this supplement, all of which illustrate the secrecy of the work at Hawkcraig and how widely it was deployed in the fight against the U-boat. Thanks to Ken Weston for providing a copy of "List of Names Borne on Books of H.M.S. "TARLAIR"", 1921, North Shields, W.J. Potts, Atlas Printing Works.

8. HMS Tarlair Bowling Green The location of a bowling green constructed at Lady Beatty's expense for the recreation of servicemen and staff stationed at Tarlair has been identified. Thank you to Gordon and Kathleen Maxwell for providing this information.

9. Louis Arthur Jones Jones, a school master from Leeds, served at HMS Tarlair. The photograph and discharge record reproduced in the supplement were loaned to the publisher by his granddaughter Kathleen Maxwell. Information on other men who served at the base is scant. The author and publisher would welcome contact from any descendants so that we can build up a more complete picture of the staff serving at the base during the war (aberdour.culture@outlook.com).

10. Silver Salver Tony Connor kindly loaned and allowed us to photograph a commemorative silver salver which was presented to G.H. Rogers, May 1919, HMS Tarlair Hydrophone Service R.N.V.R. Currently, we know nothing about the salver and its history, so would welcome any further information.

11. Album relating to the naval service of Captain Cyril Percy Ryan C.B. (Object ID 0228) This item is held in the collection of The Royal Museums Greenwich and we are grateful to them for allowing us to reproduce some of the photographs included in this collection, which were taken by Ryan while he was serving at HMS Tarlair.

12. Successful Achievements at HMS Tarlair A list of some of the major technical and operational achievements resulting from the work at HMS Tarlair is included at the end of this supplement.

1. BIR 10071/16 Report by the Duke of Buccleuch, Lord Rutherford FRS and Sir R. Paget on visits to the Experimental Station under Commander Ryan RN, Granton on September 15, 16 and 21 1915

This report, which is held by the National Archives, includes the following extracts, illustrating how well progressed Ryan's hydrophone experiments were by 1915.

On September 15th two of us, viz. Lord Rutherford and Sir R Paget, visited the Hydrophone Station at Hawks Craig Point, and listened to the sounds produced in the different hydrophones by six different ships viz a torpedo boat, two different 'drifters' separately, a 30-ton steam yacht and a paddle steamer. Unfortunately the submarines were all absent on active service.

Six out of eight experimental hydrophones were in excellent working order, though they had been in position for several months; one was temporarily inoperative. It was of an old type which had not been provided with a tapping device to free the carbon granules in case of 'packing'.

The 'natural' sounds - in the absence of moving vessels in the neighbourhood - were very slight and did not compare in intensity with those produced by the two torpedo boat destroyers at a distance of 4 or 5 miles.

The sounds of the different types of boats mentioned were clearly and easily distinguishable at ranges between 1 and 2 miles in the case of the smaller vessels, and at 3 or 4 miles in the case of the torpedo boat and the torpedo boat destroyer. Commander Ryan informed us that a submarine, submerged, gave a quite distinctive sound of intensity even greater than that due to a torpedo boat destroyer at the same distance.

2. BIR 10064/16 Report on methods of collecting sound from water and determination of the direction of sound by Lord Rutherford FRS, Sept 1915

This report, in which Rutherford discusses hydrophones, magnetophones and submarine detection, is held at the National Archives (ADM 293/7) and includes the following extracts:

In my opinion, it is important that experiments along these lines should be tried on a practical scale. If the receiving equipment can be made sufficiently sensitive, it may prove possible to follow the course of a submerged submarine by means of a swift vessel which stops her engines at intervals to permit sound observations.

The submerged buoyed hydrophone, devised by Commander Ryan, is a sensitive instrument for the detection of sound, and has already reached a stage of practical development. A system of hydrophones, connected with a central listening station on shore, has obvious advantages for detecting the approach of a submarine or other ship to the hydrophone area and by suitable spacing of the hydrophones should also give valuable information as to the position of the submarine at any moment. The hydrophone is probably the best instrument for this purpose.

The magnetophone....has the advantage of constant sensibility and reliability....It has certain advantages for special kinds of work e.g. the combination of magnetophone and mine as devised by Commander Ryan.

Rutherford was clearly impressed by Ryan and the progress that he had made at Granton. He closes his report with the following words:

In conclusion, I am of the opinion that it is of great importance that the Committee should arrange promptly for investigations along the following lines:

1...improvements in the existing methods for the detection of submarine sound.

2...relative advantages and disadvantages of different methods.....

6...practical methods for determining the direction of ships by the sound transmitted through water.

It is quite possible that these two reports were highly influential in the decision to establish a research station dedicated to developing anti-submarine technology and that command of the new establishment, HMS Tarlair, was given to Cyril Ryan because of his already productive work at Granton on hydrophone and magnetophone mine developments as reported by Rutherford.

.

3. Pages from the Journal of Petty Officer L.J. Ettles R.N.V.R. (Hydrophone Section)

Ettles trained at HMS Tarlair in summer 1918. He reports in his journal that Tarlair was the headquarters of the Hydrophone Service, construction work was still ongoing in 1918, the work was "top secret", it rained a lot and moustaches were not allowed!

On April 23rd 1918 I left my happy home and loved ones to join the R.N.V.R. (Hydrophone section). Having reported to HMS Helican early in the morning of the 23rd April we were dispatched to headquarters at Aberdour (Fifeshire).

We arrived there in the course of the afternoon and were immediately given a lecture upon the great importance of this class of work. Being of a secret nature we were debarred from speaking to anyone outside the service on the subject.

Several of our company having moustaches were told that no lip adornments were permitted and some got a quick shift.

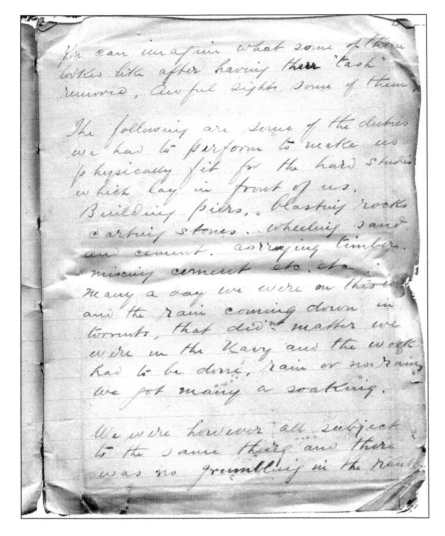

You can imagine what some of them looked like after having their "tash" removed. Awful sights some of them.

The following are some of the duties we had to perform to make us physically fit for the hard studies which lay in front of us. Building piers, blasting rocks, carting stones, wheeling sand and cement, carrying timber, mixing cement, etc., etc. Many a day we were on this work and the rain coming down in torrents, that didn't matter we were in the Navy and the work had to be done, rain or no rain, we got many a soaking. We were however all subject to the same thing and there was no grumbling in the ranks.

One day it was particularly bad and we were all soaked with the heavy rain, we "egged on" one of the P.O.s to approach the C.O. and ask him if we might be allowed to go and get a change of clothes. He went, to our great surprise but was calmly informed that he was in the Navy and had to stick it, that was sufficient, we toiled on until five o'clock at night and then made a dash.

The first work was very trying but we soon got accustomed to it. This rough work lasted for three weeks then we commenced our real work "Studies".

The next six weeks was hard graft. After the first two or three days of lectures we could see that we were in for something.

As a section we were determined to master it. (A section consists of six men)

We seemed to get into deeper water every lecture we got, not having fully digested the former days lecture. Every time we came out of the lecture hall we used to say, "The mist is getting thicker" and so it was - quite a maze.

However we stuck to it and eventually we got the thread of it and just before the examination came off we all felt we had a fair hold of the theory.

We all passed out with an average of 88% which our superiors said was excellent. We had to study every spare five minutes.

Having passed our exams successfully we were put on to practical work, which was much more interesting. A day or two at this work showed us the real importance of the theoretical classes, we could follow the building-up of the various instruments quite easily - everything seemed to come quite naturally.

We continued at this work until we got orders to pack up our gear. We were told that we were going on Foreign Service - Port Said. Before going they gave us six days leave which was very enjoyable. Too soon these days went past and we were back at headquarters waiting instructions. We had to wait three weeks before the final word came.

4. Hamilton Harty

In the following abstract from "Hamilton Harty Musical Polymath" by Jeremy Dibble (The Boydell Press, Woodbridge, 2013) Hamilton Harty recalls his work in the Hydrophone Service.

Interviewed by The Sun newspaper in Australia in 1934, during a rehearsal in Sydney, Harty recalled some of his work with the hydrophone station:

"The hydrophone service was one of the "hush" services of the Admiralty and called for skilled tonal development by the listener, a kind of discriminating and musical A. B., who could distinguish the throb of a ship's engine from the more rhythmic and subdued beat of the Diesel engines of the submarine.

The listener worked in a room surrounded by delicate instruments, not unlike the operator in the wireless room of a ship.

A cable, either from the shore or running out from the survey ship, picked up the vibrations, magnified them and sent them to the discerning ear of the listener.

Still, we accounted for many submarines during the war, and if not successful in sending them to their doom, warned ships of their proximity."

(The Sun, 6th June 1934)

Lieutenant Harty 1917

5. The Admiral Beatty Letters

The full transcripts of these two letters written by David Beatty to his wife Ethel can be found in "The Life and Times of David Beatty, Admiral of The Fleet" by Rear-Admiral W.S.Chambers (Hodder and Stoughton 1951).

An early account of the detection of a German U-boat in the Forth:

On 15th March 1915 Beatty writes: *"Great excitement, everyone very busy. Submarine has been knocking at the door all day, and they have located him near Oxcars with microphone. What a pity Ryan isn't here to work the microphone."* This letter clearly indicates that the hydrophones and other equipment developed by Ryan were already deployed and proving useful in early 1915.

Experiments to develop wireless controlled Motor Launches:

In a letter written on 6th May 1917 from The Grand Fleet at Scapa Flow to his wife in Aberdour Beatty comments that he is *"glad to hear that Ryan was getting on with aeroplane control. He certainly does work hard, and I wish everybody was as keen as he is"*. Beatty is probably referring to experiments in which a motor launch was set up to be remotely controlled from the seaplane.

In his photograph album Cyril Ryan captioned this photograph "NYKR (see page 12) (W/T control from seaplane)".

© National Maritime Museum, Greenwich, London

That the system was successful can be judged from the following account from "Hush; or, The hydrophone service" by H.W.Wilson (Mills and Boon 1920): *The business on which this seaplane went up, as often as not, was wireless control ... on these occasions there was something unnatural about the little motor launch ... Suddenly she throbs exhaltantly and dashes off as on some settled purpose. She has been started by the seaplane, and will be steered, controlled and stopped by the same.*

Ryan was assisted in these trials by Captain Michael Wemyss, described by H.W.Wilson *"as an experimenter in wireless control"*.

It is not clear what the ultimate aims of these experiments were, but it must have occurred to the imaginative Ryan that wireless controlled torpedoes launched from boats or planes could prove a very effective weapon. The German navy is known to have used remote controlled launches to attack and ram shipping. The *Fernlenkboote* was a remote-controlled motorboat, 17m long, carrying 70 kg of explosives, which was steered directly at its targets. These boats were controlled from a shore station via a spooled cable – the advantage of wireless control is clear.

6. Alexander Crichton Mitchell: Indicator Loop Trials

This report was written for this supplement by Dr Richard Walding, Research Fellow, Griffith University, Australia. Email richard@walding.com. Further information about indicator loops and Mitchell can be found at Richard's

webpages indicatorloops.com, and indicatorloops.com/mitchell.htm.

While Captain Ryan was experimenting on hydrophones at the Hawkcraig Admiralty Experimental Station at Aberdour in 1915, he was approached by a Professor of Physics about using the facilities to do a novel type of submarine detection. The physicist was Dr Alexander Crichton Mitchell who had only recently returned from 24 years' service to the Maharaja of Travancore (now Kerala) in southern India. Mitchell was a graduate of Edinburgh University and had accepted the post in India in 1890. He taught Physics and Mathematics at the Maharaja's College and was such a success that he was appointed Director of Public Instruction there – the highest educational position in the State. His physics background made him the ideal candidate for the post of Director of the Royal Observatory as well.

In 1912 Mitchell retired and returned to his family in Edinburgh on a very generous lifetime pension. He was at somewhat of a loose end and chose to become an Honorary Research Fellow at Edinburgh University, and a Committee Member of the Royal Society of Edinburgh (RSE). Just after the start of the war, the RSE was contemplating how it could assist in scientific research to help the war effort. It was well known that German U-Boats began coming into Firth of Forth up to Inchkeith Boom defenses. But the events of April 1915 certainly heightened RSE's drive: on the 21st the Swedish steamer *Ruth* from Leith was torpedoed by a U-Boat off May Island [1] and then a week later the German Professor of Ship Construction Dr Flamm wrote in the German newspaper *Vossische Zeitung* that the U-Boat would destroy The British Empire by restricting trade, particularly by blocking key ports such as the Firth of Forth [2].

On 7th June 1915 the RSE received a donation from a very generous benefactor providing funds for the purpose of investigating methods of detecting German submarines. This galvanised Mitchell who volunteered to undertake antisubmarine research in the Forth.

On 25th June permission was given to Mitchell by the Admiralty and The Leith Dock Commission for him to conduct experiments off West Pier, Leith. The list of war deaths of Cambridge men in *The Times* that same day shook them all.

Mitchell remembered an incident during some research into the conductivity of ice in 1886. He was on the roof of the Physics building in Edinburgh when an aurora in the northern sky sent his galvanometer haywire. He tucked away in his mind that changes in earth's magnetism would produce an electric current in a loop of wire. Back to 1915 in Leith: Mitchell suspended a loop of bell wire vertically over the side of the pier and waited for a steel ship to pass. A tiny current was registered on his galvanometer. He then put the loop horizontally on the seafloor and obtained a much larger reading. The electrical interference from Leith trams was a problem, but he solved this by twisting the loop into a figure-of-eight. This became the basis for his "indicator loop". His work continued until 20th August and his results were reported to the RSE and were sent on to the Board of Investigation and Research in London (where they lay for three years).

Mitchell wanted to continue his trials with a bigger loop and a submarine. On 20th August Mitchell met with Cmdr. Haggard (OIC HMS *Vulcan*) and Captain Ryan at Hawkcraig to arrange for loop equipment to be taken to the deep water off Inchkeith. Ryan provided some of his hydrophone cable (Service Pattern 841B with gutta percha insulation) and access to the British sub "B3". Mitchell spent most of the day at Inchkeith and over the next few weeks trialled his indicator loop in a more realistic situation. He had spent a grand total of £12 on his work by this stage. The results were a success and an indicator loop cable (4 core armoured lead sheathed) was later laid across the Forth. However, as Adm. Roger Keyes noted: electrical interference from the Edinburgh to Leith trams spoilt the results and the loop was removed [3].

Mitchell's work was finished. On 17th April 1916 he was appointed Superintendent of the Eskdalemuir Magnetical Observatory 100 km south of Edinburgh. His "loop" report for the RSE lay dormant in London until Professor William Bragg read through the old files and found it. Bragg began a program of loop research when he moved his team from Hawkcraig to Harwich in January 1917 but more than a year had been lost. In November 1919 Mitchell obtained some of the loop cable from Hawkcraig (for free) for use in his terrestrial magnetism research program at Eskdalemuir. Anti-submarine loop research continued in the interwar period and at the outset of WW2 loops were laid in British and Dominion ports all over the world. Mitchell died in April 1952 in Edinburgh at the age of 87.

1. *The Times*, Monday, Apr 26, 1915; pg. 5

2. *The Times* Friday, Apr 30, 1915; pg. 8.

3. "The naval memoirs of Admiral of the fleet Sir Roger Keyes: Scapa Flow to the Dover Straits, 1916-1918" E. P. Dutton & Co., 1935, page 145. Keyes said that they were then successfully used with mines (in 1918 probably at Dover).

7. Honour and Service Rolls: records of some "Tarlair" men

The hydrophone technology developed at HMS Tarlair to counter the U-boat threat was deployed not just around the British coast but also much further afield. This is made clear in "Rolls of Honour and Service" for the Great War, some of which include the service records of men trained at the base, for example, the **"Aberdeen University Roll of Service in the Great War 1914-1919"** includes the following two entries:

KESTING, ERNEST CHARLES .... *Petty Officer (1ˢᵗ Class), R.N.V.R. (Hydrophone Service), 27 Aug. 1917. Served in HMS "Tarlair," H.M. Trawler "Sea Sweeper", "Emergency Hydrophone Patrol", Hydrophone Flotilla;* **_Home, Malta, Adriatic, Aegean, Mudros, Constantinople,_** *Aug 1917-Feb 1919. Final Rank, Petty Officer.*

SMITH, ALFRED JAMES ... *Sub-Lieut., R.N.V.R., 25 Aug. 1917. Hydrophone duties,* **_Firth of Forth_**, *Aug. 1917 - Jan. 1919. Final Rank, Lieutenant.*

The following entry from the **"Dunfermline High School, Pupils and Staff, Roll of Honour"** stresses both the "secret" nature of the work at Hawkcraig as well as its widespread deployment:

TRAILL, DAVID ... *Petty Officer, Hydrophone-Instructor, R.N.V.R.* (**Secret Service**). *Joined HMS "Tarlair" April 1918.* **_Aberdour, Greenmore Point, Ireland, Mediterranean_**, *Aug. – Nov. 1918 (**Malta** and **S. Italy**). Demobilised 3ʳᵈ Feb. 1919.*

It is a tribute to the skill and inventiveness of the group of people assembled at HMS Tarlair that from some simple experiments at Granton docks a technology was developed which was considered to be so important for the successful pursuit of the war that it was "rolled out" across the naval battle front wherever the U-boat was considered a threat. This is an even more remarkable feat considering the advances which were simultaneously being made at HMS Tarlair in other fields, such as remote wireless control of vehicles (and toys!), optical communications (the photophone), as well as Crichton Mitchell's anti-submarine loops.

List of Names Borne on Books of H.M.S. "TARLAIR.", downloadable from www.aberdourculture.org.uk, includes information on many Tarlair men.

8. HMS Tarlair Bowling Green

Another 'heritage site' in Aberdour to be associated with the Tarlair project has recently been identified. We can now say with some certainty that the area of levelled garden-ground lying between the Masonic Lodge and Micklegarth, the bungalow at 72A High Street in Wester Aberdour, is the last visible trace of the bowling green constructed at Lady Beatty's expense for the recreation of servicemen and staff stationed at Tarlair. An earlier account had suggested that the intended beneficiaries were the crews of coastal batteries guarding the approaches to Rosyth, but growing awareness of the extent and nature of the anti-submarine programme undertaken here makes it far more likely that it was one of Tarlair's leisure facilities. According to information supplied several years ago by Mr Stoddart, who was long responsible for the upkeep of village thoroughfares and fabric, the material required for the bowling green was derived from the grounds of Aberdour Castle. It is therefore not surprising that, whenever flower beds were being dug in the relevant areas of the bungalow garden, the presence of late-medieval pottery was noted in the uppermost level, while shards of 'Victorian' china were found only in the lower layers - a reversal of normal stratification.

More remarkable still was the surprising discovery in Royal Navy records that Louis Arthur Jones, the paternal grandfather of a current occupier of Micklegarth, had served on the staff of Tarlair in its closing phase!

9. Louis Arthur Jones *(pictured left)*

Jones was a schoolteacher, and later headmaster, in Leeds. In Sept. 1918 he was drafted to the R.N.V.R. and posted to the Hydrophone Service serving at HMS Tarlair in Aberdour. It is quite possible that he was selected for these duties due to his teaching experience and academic abilities, which were well suited to the work at HMS Tarlair. The relatively late date of his posting shows that the base was still active up until the very end of the war. This photograph and the copy of Louis's discharge papers (reproduced below) were made available by Louis's granddaughter.

10. Silver Salver

Tony Connor kindly allowed us to photograph this Commemorative Silver Salver.

If anyone reading this knows anything about the salver or G.H.Rogers, please contact aberdour.culture@outlook.com.

11. Album relating to the naval service of Captain Cyril Percy Ryan

More information relating to the album can be found at http://collections.rmg.co.uk/collections/objects/537330.html.

We are grateful to Royal Museums Greenwich for allowing us to reproduce some of the photographs included in this collection, which were taken by Ryan while he was serving at HMS Tarlair.

© National Maritime Museum, Greenwich, London
Captain Cyril Percy Ryan pictured in the garden of Hawkcraig Cottage, Aberdour, were he lived while serving at HMS Tarlair.

© National Maritime Museum, Greenwich, London
HMS Tarlair (March 1917) Note: in foreground, tripod mounted
hydrophones. These hydrophones would be lowered to the sea bed and
connected by cables to a shore based listening station.

© National Maritime Museum, Greenwich, London
HMS Tarlair (January 1919)

Some of the "huts" at HMS Tarlair This photograph was probably taken from the Observation Tower pictured below and has been annotated by Captain Ryan to show the uses of some of the huts.

Observation Tower, possibly with Ryan's family in the foreground

© National Maritime Museum, Greenwich, London
View of HMS Tarlair showing ships and submarine

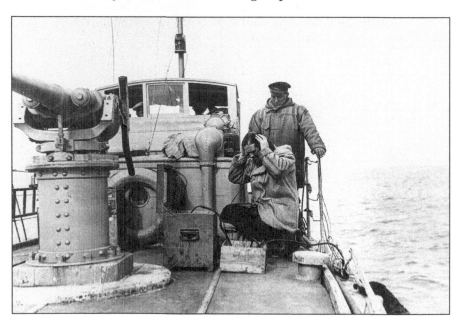

© National Maritime Museum, Greenwich, London
Drifter hydrophone set in use

12. Successful Achievements at HMS Tarlair

Scientific and technical developments

Proved that the **velocity of sound in the sea** was approximately four and half times that in air.

Development of underwater sound detection: by the end of 1918 very significant progress had been achieved, including detecting the noise of a large ship's propeller at 12 miles, inventing methods of obtaining sound direction underwater and producing a ship towed **"Fish" Hydrophone** containing a **remotely controlled unidirectional hydrophone**.

Development of Magnetophone mines (making use of the magnetophone and/or hydrophone): these accounted for the destruction of two U-boats and possibly two others. The last U-boat to be sunk in the First World War was UB116. She was destroyed on 28th October 1918 when passing over the magnetophone minefield at Scapa Flow.

Development of Depth-sounding bombs as part of the programme.

Development of Indicator Loop methods of submarine detection: these were proved and perfected by Alexander Crichton Mitchell while working with Ryan at Hawkcraig.

Introduction of the Photophone (a method of communicating across long distance by the modulation of a beam of light by speech) to the programme of scientific investigations: patented after the war by Rankine for recording speech on film, which was used in the development of the first "talking" movies/films.

Experiments into Remote / Wireless Control: these included modifying a Motor Launch (NYKR), first so that it could be controlled remotely from land or another ship and then demonstrating independent control from a flying plane. Ryan probably also produced the first remote controlled toy!

Proved that **Seaplanes** were useful in **detecting submarines from the air.**

Naval achievements – training and operational

Hawkcraig was **the Navy's main hydrophone and research training base.** **1,090 officers** and **2,731 ratings** attended courses there or were trained by instructors from Hawkcraig. By the end of the war HMS Tarlair numbered 650 ratings and 120 officers, manning hydrophone stations at home and abroad.

31 Shore hydrophone stations were set up round the coast of the British Isles and further abroad. Ships were also attached to Hawkcraig.

Tarlair staff **fitted submarines with hydrophones** and issued special sets of hydrophones to the **1,500 drifters and motor launches in the Auxiliary patrol.**

The **final tally** of World War I proved that at least six U-boats sank as a direct result of hydrophone contacts (UC3, UC49, UC66, U78, UB107 and UB115). In 1918 there were 54 sightings of U-boats **in which hydrophones played a part**. The "deterrent value" in restricting U-boat operations should not be undervalued.

References and other source material

"The Hawkcraig Experiments" A. B. Wood, Sound, Vol.3, no.3, 1962

"The beginnings of Submarine Detection" Brian Head, Warship, Vol.9, 1989

"Avian Anti-Submarine Warfare Proposals in Britain, 1915-18: The Admiralty and Thomas Mills" David A. H. Wilson, International Journal of Naval History, Volume 5, Number 1, 2006

Royal Commission on the Ancient and Historical Monuments of Scotland, Seaplane Base (First World War) Canmore ID 331241/Site No. NT18SE76

"Hush; or, The hydrophone service" Herbert Wilson (1866-1940), Pub. London, Mills & Boon Ltd., 1920

"Aberdour in The First Half of The Twentieth Century", articles in Aberdour Village News, Diana Maxwell, 1997

The photograph collection of the National Submarine Museum, Gosport

The photograph collection of the Fleet Air Arm Museum, Yeovilton

"Defeating the U-boat – Inventing Anti-Submarine Warfare" Jan S. Breemer, Naval College Newport Papers, No. 36, Naval War College Press, 2010

"RN Station Hawkcraig, Aberdour, Fife, during World War I", an album of approx. 280 contemporary photographs, National Maritime Museum Archive, Object ID ALB0324

"Album relating to the service of Captain Cyril Percy Ryan C.B.", an album of approx. 180 contemporary photographs relating to Ryan's service at Hawkcraig, National Maritime Museum Archive, Object ID ALB0228

"Oral reminiscences of A. B. Wood, 1960", taped recorded interview (approx. 2hrs) American Institute of Physics, Niels Bohr Library Archive

Records held in the National Archives. Records relating to HMS Tarlair include ADM 218/1, ADM Division 13, ADM218/81, ADM218/82, ADM218/74, ADM218/103, ADM218/77, ADM293/4, ADM218/79, ADM218/78, ADM218/1/2, ADM218/76, ADM218/75, ADM218/1/4

"Seek and Strike; Sonar, anti-submarine warfare and the Royal Navy 1914-1954" Willem Hackmann, Pub. London HMSO, 1984

Journal of the Royal Navy Scientific Service. "Albert Beaumont Wood OBE, DSc Memorial Number" Vol.20, No.4, 1965

"The U-Boat War, 1914-18" Edwin A Gray, Pub. Combined Books, 1994

Acknowledgements

I would like to thank for their contributions and support: Lewis Banks, John

Burrell, Alison Chapman, Tony Connor, Jeremy Dibble, Jose Luis Eglinton, Jane Halleran, Arthur Lloyd, Gordon and Kathleen Maxwell, Tom Nisbet, Mike Porter, Ian Stevens, John Taylor, Bob Trillo, Richard Walding, Ken Weston, Dave Wilkinson, Annie Worrall and the late William Cuthill, John Henderson and Rena McLauchlan.

William Cuthill died in 2008 at the age of 94 as is recorded in this memorial stone in Aberdour graveyard

And also: Aberdour Cultural Association, Aberdour Community Council, Burntisland Heritage Trust, Fife Council, Fleet Air Arm Museum, ForthRoad Ltd, Heritage Lottery Fund Scotland, National Maritime Museum Archive, National Submarine Museum.

Disclaimer

In telling the story of HMS Tarlair, the author has tried to ensure the accuracy of the information in this booklet. Despite this, it is possible that some errors may have slipped in undetected, for which she apologises. Readers aware of errors are invited to contact the publisher (Aberdour Cultural Association – aberdour.culture@outlook.com) so that future editions may be corrected.

Local History

The publication of this booklet is part of an ongoing "not for profit" local history project within the village of Aberdour, Fife. This "informal" community-based project involves a number of local groups and individuals. Readers wanting to know more about this project or who have a contribution that they would like to make are invited to contact the publisher (Aberdour Cultural Association – aberdour.culture@outlook.com).